To aspiring ballet dancers
and french speakers everywhere.

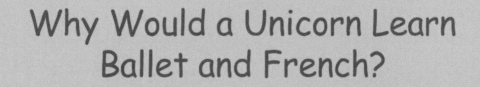

Why Would a Unicorn Learn Ballet and French?

Unicorn Learning Series

Powered by love

Rachel Jessop
&
Tammy Appenzellar

How this book came to be

Shona inspired this book with her love for ballet and her desire to understand the meaning of the French words used in her classes.

As her mum, Rachel, loves helping Shona to grow and to learn, she reached out and found Tammy, who is fluent in French.

It was love at first sight for the three of them! And they laughed and giggled their way through the making of this book.

Shona believes that learning is key to growing, and wants to share all the amazing things she learned in this beautiful collaboration.

Many hours and much love was poured into this book to give you a taste of the fabulous adventure of dance and French rolled together.
May it bless you.

With love and encouragement,

Shona & Rachel & Tammy

The real Shona
&
the real Dreamy

Hi, my name's Dreamy and I'm a unicorn, welcome to my forest! Unicorns do some pretty cool stuff.

Like helping people and granting wishes. I love it so much, I really can't help myself!

So, there I was one day
just hanging around,
doing my unicorn thing,
when my friend Shona
came to visit.

Hi, Shona!

Oh hey, Dreamy. How are you?

I'm good! How are you doing?

Well, I'm having a bad day, says Shona.

Oh no! What's wrong? asks Dreamy

Well, I really want to learn ballet and I really want to learn what all the cool French words mean, and I don't know how to do it.

You don't know how to do it?
asks Dreamy.

No! Can you please help me?

What's a unicorn to do!
Looks like it's time to grant
some wishes!

Dreamy the Unicorn then
shakes her rainbow mane,
whinnies loudly, and shoots
stars out of her horn...

4

Tah-dah! Here is your ballet school and your french-speaking ballet teacher!

Bonjour, Shona. That means hello in French, says Tammy.

Bonjour, replies Shona.

I'm excited to meet you and to teach you about ballet and French!

Ballet means ballet, it's the same word. Ballerine means ballerina.

Let's go inside! says Dreamy.

Yes, this ballet school is really dreamy, Dreamy! says Shona.

On y va, that means let's go! says Tammy.

On y va! exclaims Shona.

Here we are inside the ballet school, says Tammy, and here is your sac, that means bag in French, Shona.

Oh, wow! Sac! Thanks.

Yes, and let's learn the names of the things in your ballet sac.

Pronunciation is fun and funny!
It takes time to get it right,
be ready to laugh at yourself,
and keep prancing... I mean
practicing, and you will get it.
Unicorns love to laugh at
themselves!

You're absolutely right,
Dreamy! says Tammy.

This is the ballet gear most kids have in their sac, Shona.

Body
Leotard

Kit de couture
Sewing kit

Jupe
Skirt

Goûter
Snacks

Collants
Tights

Bouteille d'eau
Water bottle

I could use a drink of water right now! It's always good to stay hydrated! exclaims Dreamy.

Chaussures
Shoes

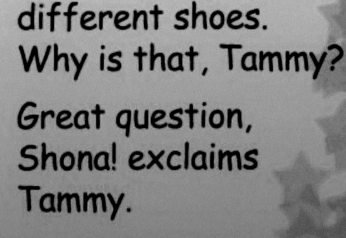

I see the kids have different shoes. Why is that, Tammy?

Great question, Shona! exclaims Tammy.

There are different types of chaussures. You can get canvas or leather; it's really a personal preference.

Toile is canvas and cuir is leather.

Me, I just have hooves! says Dreamy.

Lastly, let's talk about pointe shoes. Pointe.

They are beautiful! exclaims Shona. You get to wear those when you're advanced, says Tammy.

Oh, I can't wait to wear those pointe shoes! gushes Shona.

Doigts
Fingers

Mains
Hands

Tête
Head

Bras
Arms

Jambes
Legs

Genoux
Knees

Pieds
Feet

Doigts de pieds
Toes

Now, we have learned about the parts of the body in French, says Tammy.

This little piggy went to market... oops, nope! Unicorns don't have toes either!

What about hair? asks Shona.

Take it away, Dreamy! says Tammy.

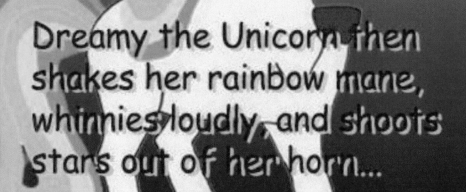

Dreamy the Unicorn then shakes her rainbow mane, whinnies loudly, and shoots stars out of her horn...

Hair we are! laughs Dreamy.

Now, here are some things you will
need to put up your hair for ballet,
says Tammy.

Élastique à cheveux ⭐ Hair ties

Chignon donut ⭐ Donut hair bun

Donut eat these! jokes Dreamy.

Épingle à cheveux ⭐ Bobby pins

Filet à chignon ⭐ Hairnet

Laque ⭐ Hair spray

Most hair buns usually start
with a unicorn tail... oops,
I mean ponytail! laughs
Dreamy.

I love to brush horses' manes and tails, says Shona.

You're not getting your hands on my mane! But, check this out!

16

Wow, look at the colors shooting out of your horn, Dreamy! I love them!

All those colors are my colors and that makes me wanna dance! shouts Dreamy.

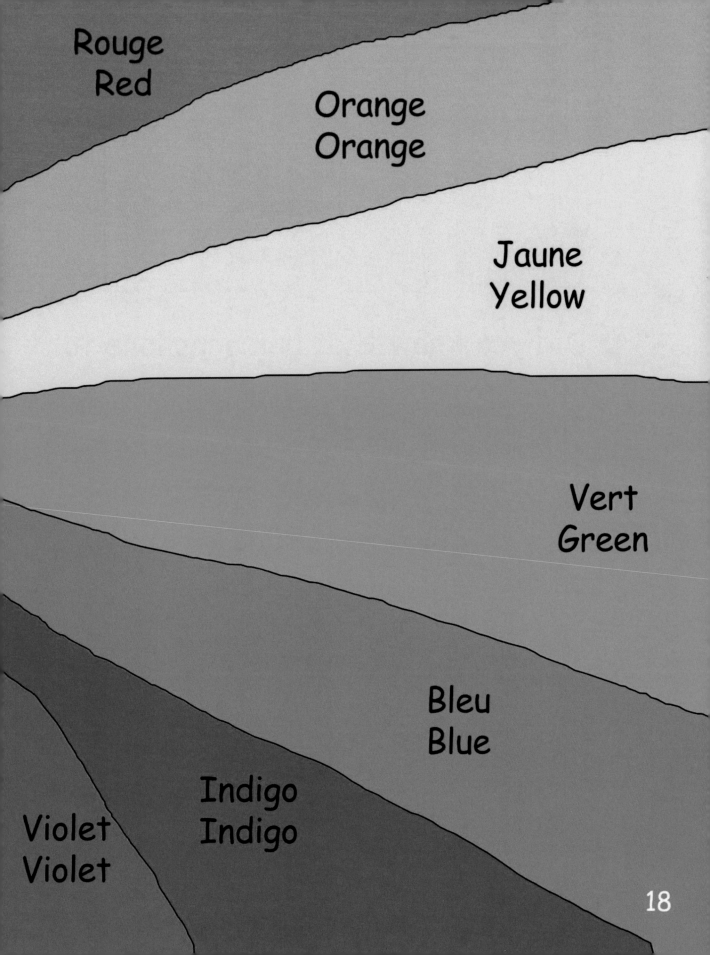

Did you know that unicorns love to dance?

Whaaaaat! Unicorns love to dance?! exclaims Shona.

'Stayin' alive, Stayin' alive!... ah ah ah ah...'

Let's learn a couple of French words, and get dancing!

Barre à ballet ⭐ Ballet Bar

Piste de danse ⭐ Dance Floor

Miroir ⭐ Mirror

Miroir, miroir on the wall... oops, nope! Wrong story! Ha ha! jokes Dreamy.

I'm a little nervous, says Shona, what do I do when I get to class?

Let's talk about ballet étiquette, says Tammy.

Etta what? asks Shona.

You ate a cat? asks Dreamy.

No, sillies! étiquette means rules you follow.

Oh, étiquette means keep off the grass, jokes Shona.

Stop mentioning grass, I'm still hungry! exclaims Dreamy.

So, if étiquette means how we act, then how do I act in ballet class? asks Shona.

Each ballet school has their own étiquette, and the teacher will tell you what to do, says Tammy.

Cool, what do we learn next? asks Shona.

How about ballet positions? says Tammy.

These positions are the ABCs of ballet.

Oh, how exciting, can you teach me?

Avec plaisir, with pleasure, Shona.

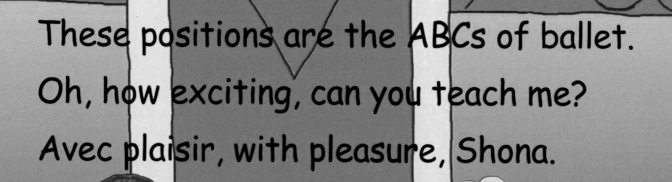

Première
First

Séconde
Second

Troisième
Third

Quatrième
Fourth

Cinquième
Fifth

Sixième
Sixth

Oh la la, exclaims Dreamy, I'm all hooves! Maybe music would help me?

I love dancing to music. How do you say that in French, Tammy? asks Shona.

J'adore danser avec la musique.

Hey, let's count to the beat! exclaims Dreamy.

Bien sûr, of course!

The basic eight-count beat of all music

Un	★	One
Deux	★	Two
Trois	★	Three
Quatre	★	Four
Cinq	★	Five
Six	★	Six
Sept	★	Seven
Huit	★	Eight

un, deux, trois, quatre, cinq, six, sept, huit
one, two, three, four, five, six, seven, eight

This makes me want to dance!
Ahhhh, I really wish I could snap my hooves to the beat! exclaims Dreamy.

It makes me wanna dance too! shouts Shona.

Shona, would you like to watch a
real ballet production? asks Tammy.

I would love to!

Dreamy the Unicorn then shakes her rainbow mane, whinnies loudly, and shoots stars out of her horn...

Wow, this is so pretty! says Shona.

Pretty super amazing! says Dreamy.

Très magnifique! says Tammy.

What does that mean? asks Shona.

Très magnifique means very magnificent.

Bravo!

I loved the turning, the costumes, the music, the back-drops, there is so much to see! Wasn't it fabulous?

Yes, it was, Shona. Would you like to become a ballerine in a production?

I would love to!

Great! To get into a ballet production, you start with an audition, explains Tammy.

What's an audition? asks Shona.

Take it away, Dreamy!

Dreamy the Unicorn then shakes her rainbow mane, whinnies loudly, and shoots stars out of her horn...

An audition is where you dance in front of adults who will give a part to each dancer.

I'm a little nervous, whispers Shona.

An audition can be fun! Just do your best and enjoy it.

Ok, I'll try that.

So, Tammy, how do dancers get so glamorous looking on stage?

They get it from me!
laughs Dreamy. I
master the glamour!
I'm the Glamour
Master!

Dreamy the Unicorn then
shakes her rainbow mane,
whinnies loudly, and shoots
stars out of her horn...

34

To look extraordinarily glamorous, it's important to wear makeup to highlight your features, or you can look very pale on stage under those bright lights, explains Tammy.

Oh la la! exclaims Dreamy, it sounds right up my ally, I know how to do extra-ordinary!

Then, let's get all glamour, glamorous! says Tammy. We will put rouge on your cheeks. Did you know that lipstick is called rouge à levres? That means rouge for your lips. Next, we will put on some eyeliner and mascara...

I love your makeup, Dreamy, says Shona.

Unicorns are naturally glamorous! And we love playing dress up... So, now I will show you the final touch, exclaims Dreamy.

La pièce de résistance, says Tammy.

Dreamy the Unicorn then shakes her rainbow mane, whinnies loudly, and shoots stars out of her horn...

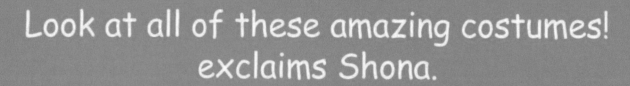

Look at all of these amazing costumes! exclaims Shona.

Ohhh, I feel like a Fairy Unicorn-Mother! Everyone looks fabulous! Now, to the stage!

Dreamy the Unicorn then shakes her rainbow mane, whinnies loudly, and shoots stars out of her horn...

38

Why are we all standing together on stage holding hands? whispers Shona.

We are going to do our final bow and curtsy, replies Tammy.

The audience is clapping, this is all very exciting! gushes Shona.

How do you say curtsy in French, Tammy?

Révérence.

Révérence, ohhh, that sounds pretty, says Shona.

Well done, Shona, what a journey we've had learning tons of stuff about ballet and French, says Tammy.

Oh, I loved all of this so much! Thank you, Tammy, for everything you taught me, I can't wait to practice and get better, says Shona.

Now it's time for me to go. Au revoir! See you next time, says Tammy.

Au revoir! replies Shona.
Au revoir, Tammy! says Dreamy.

Dreamy the Unicorn then shakes her rainbow mane, whinnies loudly, and shoots stars out of her horn...

Dreamy, you're the best Fairy Unicorn-Mother ever! Thank you so much, I really loved everything that I learned.

That's what unicorns are for!

Do you think we could have another adventure together? asks Shona.

I have a few more ideas up my sleeve... I mean, up my horn!

Meet me back here, same unicorn time, same unicorn place!

But right now... can you hear that?

No, what is it?

My stomach is calling.... time to eat some grass!

Au revoir!

Au revoir!

44

LE FIN

THE END

French to English Glossary

Just in case you want to
practice your French
some more!

Bonjour ⭐ Hello
Ballet ⭐ Ballet
Ballerine ⭐ Ballerina
On y va ⭐ Let's go

Sac ⭐ Bag

Body ⭐ Leotard
Collants ⭐ Tights
Jupe ⭐ Skirt
Bouteille d'eau ⭐ Water bottle
Goûter ⭐ Snack
Kit de couture ⭐ Sewing kit
Chaussures ⭐ Shoes

Toile ⭐ Canvas
Cuir ⭐ Leather
Pointe ⭐ Pointe

Tête ⭐ Head
Bras ⭐ Arms
Mains ⭐ Hands
Doigts ⭐ Fingers
Jambes ⭐ Legs
Genoux ⭐ Knees
Pieds ⭐ Feet
Doigts de pieds ⭐ Toes

Cheveux ⭐ Hair
Élastique à cheveux ⭐ Hair ties
Chignon donut ⭐ Donut hair bun
Épingle à cheveux ⭐ Bobby pins
Filet à chignon ⭐ Hair net
Laque ⭐ Hair spray

Rouge ⭐ Red
Orange ⭐ Orange
Jaune ⭐ Yellow
Vert ⭐ Green
Bleu ⭐ Blue
Indigo ⭐ Indigo
Violet ⭐ Violet

French to English Glossary

Just in case you want
to practice your French
some more!

Barre à ballet ⭐ Ballet bar
Piste de danse ⭐ Dance floor
Miroir ⭐ Mirror

Étiquette ⭐ Etiquette

Avec plaisir ⭐ With pleasure
Première ⭐ First
Séconde ⭐ Second
Troisième ⭐ Third
Quatrième ⭐ Fourth
Cinquième ⭐ Fifth
Sixième ⭐ Sixth
Oh la la ⭐ Wow

J'adore danser avec la musique ⭐
I love dancing to music

Bien sûr ⭐ Of course

Un ⭐ One
Deux ⭐ Two
Trois ⭐ Three
Quatre ⭐ Four
Cinq ⭐ Five
Six ⭐ Six
Sept ⭐ Seven
Huit ⭐ Eight

Très magnifique ⭐ Very magnificent
Bravo ⭐ Well done

Glamour ⭐ Glamorous
Pièce de résistance
Final touch, the most important piece

Révérence ⭐ Curtsy or bow

Au revoir ⭐ Until next time

Fin ⭐ The End

Made in the USA
Middletown, DE
31 May 2021

40772929R00031